WASHINGTON IRVING

P9-APF-518

RIP VAN WINKLE

Edited by:
Robert Dewsnap
Illustrations: Cornelius Scherg

EASY READERS
ER
EASY READERS

The vocabulary is based on
Michael West: A General Service List of
English Words, revised & enlarged edition 1953
Pacemaker Core Vocabulary, 1975
Salling/Hvid: English-Danish Basic Dictionary, 1970
J. A. van Ek: The Threshold Level for Modern Language
Learning in Schools, 1976

Cover layout: Mette Plesner
Cover illustration: Cornelius Scherg

1995 by Aschehoug Dansk Forlag A/S
ISBN Denmark 87-11-08824-9

Printed in Denmark by
Sangill Bogtryk & offset, 1995

WASHINGTON IRVING (1783-1859)

was born in New York, and his first book was a humorous history of that city. He travelled up the Hudson River and collected material for stories such as Rip Van Winkle. From 1815 to 1832 he travelled in Germany, Austria, France, Spain and the British Isles, collecting old stories. His intention was to use European folk-tales as the basis for American stories. In London he met the writer Sir Walter Scott, who encouraged him to write The Sketch Book of Geoffrey Crayon, Gent, from which the story in this Easy Reader is taken. The Sketch Book was highly successful, and after its publication Irving was called the inventor of the modern short story. He spent the winter of 1822-23 mainly in Dresden, Germany, where he began to write his Tales of a Traveller. It was in Granada, Spain, that he found material for his book Tales of the Alhambra. From 1842 to 1846 he was the United States ambassador to Spain, where he continued studying the legends of the Moorish (Arab) past. Irving spent his later years at his home "Sunnyside" in Tarrytown, on the Hudson River.

SOME WORKS OF
WASHINGTON IRVING

A History of New York by Diedrich Knickerbocker (1809), The Sketch Book of Geoffrey Crayon, Gent (1819-20), Bracebridge Hall (1822), Tales of a Traveller (1824), Columbus (1828), The Conquest of Granada (1829), Tales of the Alhambra (1832), A Tour of the Prairies (1835), Astoria (1836), The Adventures of Captain Bonneville (1837), Oliver Goldsmith (biography, 1849), Mahomet and His Successors (biography, 1850), George Washington (biography, 1855-59).

The Complete Works of Washington Irving appeared in 30 volumes in 1969-89.

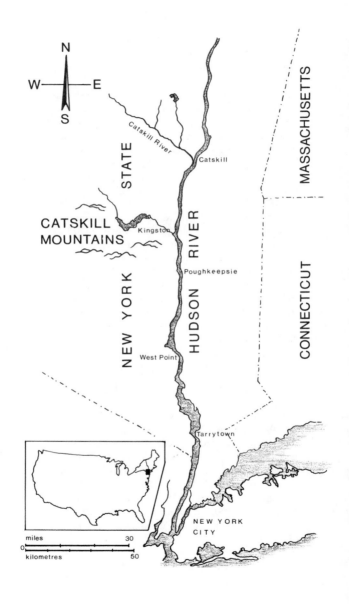

N
W — E
S

CATSKILL River

STATE

Catskill

CATSKILL
MOUNTAINS

Kingston

HUDSON RIVER

NEW YORK

Poughkeepsie

West Point

Tarrytown

NEW YORK
CITY

MASSACHUSETTS

CONNECTICUT

miles   30
0
kilometres   50

Chapter 1

Have you ever gone up the Hudson River? If so, then you will remember the high Catskill Mountains. These mountains stand like lords above the fields and rivers.

When the weather is fine and there is no 5 wind, the mountains look blue. On other days, grey clouds come up around the tops of the mountains; then, when the sun goes down, it gives a golden light to all these clouds.

At the foot of these mountains there are 10 broad green fields. Just where the fields begin, below the trees, you may see a small village. It is a very old little village. Dutch people built it many years ago.

* * *

All those years ago, the country still belonged to 15 Great Britain. At that time, there lived in that same village, in one of those very houses, a friendly, good-natured man called Rip Van Winkle. He was kind to everyone in the village, and they all liked him. 20

Rip's wife was a woman with a very sharp *tongue*. Every day you could hear her shouting

| *tongue*: see picture, page 6

tongue

angrily at her husband Rip. But Rip was a kind man, so he just sat and listened *quietly* and said nothing.

The children of the village were always very
5 happy to see Rip coming down the street. He played with the children, made little boats for them, taught them to fly *kites*, and told them long stories of *ghosts*, *witches* and Indians. The children followed him all through the village;
10 and the dogs of the village never *barked* at him.

* * *

Rip tells a story about ghosts and witches

quiet, not making much sound
bark, to give the sharp cry of a dog

6

Rip Van Winkle
flies a kite

There was only one thing wrong with Rip. He hated doing any kind of work in his own home. He was ready enough to do other kinds of work. Sometimes he sat in the cold winter rain beside the river and fished quite happily all day, even if he never caught a single fish. On other days, he went out with his *gun* and walked for hours in the Catskill Mountains.

gun

Rip was always ready to help a *neighbour*, even in the hardest work in the fields. But work in his own fields – that was something he just could not do.

His own fields, said Rip, were no good. Animals ate up the plants in his garden; and it always started to rain at the wrong time. So it was best not to work at these things at all.

Rip's children were dressed in old clothes, some of them with holes in. His son was also called Rip. This boy was dressed in old clothes too, and he was very like his father.

| *neighbour*, a person living in one of the nearest houses

Chapter 2

Rip Van Winkle was usually quite happy with his life. His only trouble was his wife's sharp tongue.

"Rip! You never do any work!" Rip's wife used to shout at him. "You never make any money! Look at your children, in these old clothes! You never think of your family!"

From morning till night, Rip's wife's tongue was always going. When she shouted at him, Rip always did the same thing: he shook his head and turned his eyes up towards the sky. Rip's wife then shouted louder than ever. When she started shouting like that, Rip used to leave the house.

And so did Wolf.

Wolf was Rip's dog. Rip's wife used to shout at Wolf as well, and she often threw things at him. Whenever she lifted her arm to throw something, Wolf ran to the door.

* * *

When Rip left the house, he used to go and look for some other men of the village. He usually found them outside a small *inn*, under the *sign*

inn, a small hotel
sign: see picture, page 11

9

sign

of *King George the Third*. Here, the men of the village used to sit through the long summer afternoons, talking quietly about the village, or telling long, sleepy stories about nothing.

Sometimes the schoolmaster, Derrick Van ⁵ Bummel, found an old newspaper and read it to the other men. Then they all put their heads together and talked about the things which had happened in the towns and cities of the outside world several months before. And all the time, ¹⁰ old Nicholas Vedder sat quietly listening.

* * *

Even when he was sitting among these men, however, the unlucky Rip was not safe from his wife. More than once, that wife of his suddenly came to the inn and started shouting at the ¹⁵ men.

King George the Third (1738-1820), George III, king of Great Britain and Ireland from 1760 to 1820

11

12

"Look at you!" Rip's wife shouted at the men. "You men never do any work! You never make any money! You just sit here at the inn all day, doing nothing!"

"What shall I do?" said poor Rip to himself. "Whatever shall I do?"

Sometimes Rip just took his gun and walked off into the woods. There he sat down at the foot of a tree and ate his food. And he always gave some of his food to Wolf.

"Poor Wolf!" said Rip. "You have a very bad life at home. But never mind! As long as I live, you will always have a friend to stand by your side!"

Then Wolf turned his eyes upon his master's face, and seemed to say the same.

Chapter 3

One day, Rip was out in the Catskill Mountains with his gun, looking for small animals for food. Again and again, his gun sounded among the trees. At last, in the late afternoon, he came
5 to one of the highest parts of the Catskill Mountains. Here he stopped and lay down on a little green hill. He looked out over the trees, and towards the great silver-coloured Hudson River which lay far below him.

10 As Rip looked round, the sun began to go down. It was time to go home, he saw, back to the sharp tongue of his wife.

Rip was just about to walk down the mountain when he heard a voice from some
15 place below him. This voice called out, "Rip Van Winkle! Rip Van Winkle!" Rip looked around, but he could only see a large black bird flying along by itself near the top of the mountain. So he turned back again, and started
20 on his way down the mountain.

But just then he heard the same cry once again, sounding through the still evening air: "Rip Van Winkle! Rip Van Winkle!" At the same time, Wolf turned his head towards the
25 sound of the cry, and the hairs on his back stood on end. Rip now began to feel strangely afraid. He looked at Wolf, then turned his head

14

15

to look down the mountain.

* * *

A little way below him on the mountain, Rip saw a small strange figure climbing up the mountain towards him. It was the figure of a little old man. The old man was climbing slowly up the mountain, carrying something heavy on his back.

"This must be someone needing help!" said Rip to himself.

So he hurried down to meet the strange new figure.

When he came closer, Rip saw that this really was a very strange little man. He was dressed like one of the old Dutchmen, from the earliest days of the village. He was carrying on his back a small *barrel*. It looked like a barrel of strong drink.

barrel

16

The little old man wanted Rip to carry the barrel for him. Rip took the barrel and put it on his back. Then the two men went up the mountain together.

As they climbed, Rip suddenly heard a low 5 sound like that of *a thunderstorm* far away over the mountains. After a minute or two, the low sound of thunder came again. The two men climbed slowly upwards. The sound of thunder

a thunderstorm

came again, and now it seemed to be very close 10 to them. Rip and the little old man walked on towards the sound of thunder, then passed between two large *rocks*. On the other side of these rocks, the two men stopped and looked down. Just below them lay a round *clearing* 15 between the trees.

rock: see picture, page 18
clearing, an open place between trees

two rocks

The whole time, Rip and the little old man had climbed without saying a word.

* * *

the

18

In the middle of the clearing, several men were playing *ninepins*. These men, too, were dressed like old Dutchmen from the earliest days of the village. Rip looked at the strange group. The men played without saying a word. The whole scene was very quiet, except for the noise of the balls. Whenever the men started playing, the balls made a noise like heavy thunder over the mountains.

As Rip and the little old man came closer, the men stopped their game and looked hard at Rip. They looked at him very strangely. They were not angry, and they were not happy. They did not open their mouths. They were almost like

pins

dead men. But all the time, their eyes looked
hard at Rip. Rip began to feel very much afraid.

The little old man now took the barrel and
told Rip to give drinks to the other men.

5   After a time, Rip began to feel less afraid
than before. He watched the strange men
playing their game of ninepins. Then, after
another little while, Rip took a little drink from
the barrel. It tasted very good, so Rip took
10 another drink, then another. After three or four
drinks, his eyes began to close. He sat down
with his back against a tree. Soon, Rip Van
Winkle was sleeping deeply.

* * *

When Rip woke up, he found himself on the small green hill further down the mountain. He looked around. It was a bright summer morning.

"Surely," thought Rip, "I have not slept here 5 all night?"

He remembered the little old man with a barrel of drink – the two large rocks – the clearing between the trees – the strange men playing ninepins – and the barrel of drink again. 10

"Ah! The drink from that barrel! That terrible drink!" thought Rip. "What shall I say now to my wife?"

He looked round for his gun – his clean,

bright gun. But all he could find was a gun that was years and years old. The gun was so old that it was falling to pieces.

"Those men!" said Rip to himself. "They 5 took my gun while I was sleeping here!"

His dog, Wolf, had gone as well. Rip shouted for his dog, but no dog came.

"I must find those men," said Rip to himself. "I shall ask them to give me back my dog and 10 gun."

* * *

When Rip stood up to walk, he found that it was difficult to move his legs.

"These mountain beds are not good for me," thought Rip. "I can hardly walk this morning!"

With some difficulty, Rip climbed up the mountain again, towards the two large rocks.

But when he got there, the two rocks had gone. There was only a large wall of rock, and Rip saw no way to get through it. There was no way through the rock to the clearing between the trees.

Again Rip called for his dog, but all he heard was the birds, in the trees and high above him in the air.

"What can I do now?" Rip asked himself. "I'm hungry, so I'll just go home for breakfast."

So Rip took the broken old gun in his hand and turned his steps towards his village home.

Chapter 4

As Rip came closer to the village, he met a number of people. But he did not know any of them. He found this surprising. Surely he knew everyone in the village and in the country
5 round about? These people were dressed in very strange clothes. Rip had never seen anyone dressed in clothes like that.

The people all looked hard at Rip. Every time

they looked at him, Rip noticed, they put their
hands up to their faces. So Rip put his hand up
to his face as well. And what did he find? He was
wearing a long grey *beard*!

Rip was now coming into the village. A ₅

beard

number of strange children were running around him, laughing and pointing at his long grey beard. The dogs, too, were all dogs that he did not know, and they barked at him as he
5 passed.

The village itself was different now. It was larger. There were streets of houses which he had never seen before. Strange names were over the doors – strange faces were at the windows –
10 everything was strange. Most of the old houses, which he had always known, were gone.

"What can have happened here?" Rip asked himself. "Have I lost my mind? Have ghosts and witches changed everything? Surely this is my
15 village? My village which I left yesterday?"

There stood the Catskill Mountains – there ran the silver Hudson River – there lay every field exactly as it had always been. Rip put his hands to his head.

20 "The drink from that barrel last night," he said to himself, "has done something terrible to my poor head!"

* * *

It was difficult to find the way to his own house. At last he found the house and stood in front of
25 it. Every moment he expected to hear the loud voice of his wife, but all was quiet. The windows

26

of the little house were broken, and the front door stood half open. A thin, hungry dog, rather like Wolf, came out from behind the house. Rip called him by name, but the dog showed his teeth and ran away. Rip was very 5 sorry to see that. "Even my own dog," he said to himself, "has forgotten me!"

Rip entered his house. His wife had always kept it in good order. But now the house was empty – no one lived there now. Rip called out 10 loudly for his wife and children, but all he heard in the empty rooms was the sound of his own voice. Then all was quiet again.

* * *

"I know!" said Rip to himself. "I'll go to the inn and talk to my friends." 15

But when he got there, the little old inn, too, was gone. A large hotel now stood there in its place. Over the door stood the name: THE UNION HOTEL. The great tree, that in the old days used to keep the hot sun off the quiet little 20 Dutch inn, was gone too. In its place, there was now a tall *pole*, and on this pole a new, strange *flag* was flying.

| *pole, flag*: see picture, page 28

flag

flagpole

"Whatever has happened here?" Rip asked himself.

On the hotel sign, Rip saw the same round, red face of King George, under which he had so
5 often sat and talked quietly with his friends. But even this sign was now different. The red coat was now blue, the head had a hat on it, and underneath stood the name GENERAL WASHINGTON.

10 As usual, there was a crowd of people outside the inn, but once again Rip knew none of them. All the faces were new and strange to him. Also, the people were talking much faster and more loudly than before. In the old days, Rip and his
15 friends had always talked quietly and peacefully together.

Rip looked for old Nicholas Vedder, sitting and quietly listening; but he could not find Nicholas anywhere. Rip hoped to see Van
20 Bummel, the teacher, reading out news from

28

some old newspaper. But there was no Van Bummel.

Instead of these old friends of Rip Van Winkle's, a thin man stood there talking about the war – about an *election* – and about members of *Congress*. All these things were new to Rip. The thin man talked more and more about these things, but the words meant nothing to Rip.

* * *

The men began to look at Rip Van Winkle as he stood there. The thin man came up to him and asked him, "Which side do you like best?"

Rip just looked at him.

Another man asked him, "Which is your party? Are you a *Federal* or a *Democrat?*"

Rip did not understand this question either.

A third man with a big hat on his head then came up to Rip. He asked Rip, "Why have you come to the election with a gun in your hand? Do you want to make trouble in the village?"

election, a time when people choose the government of their country
Congress, the law-making body of the United States of America
Federal, Democrat: these are the names of the two political parties

"I am sorry!" cried Rip. "I am a poor quiet man, and I have lived all my life in this village. I am happy to live here under good King George. God save the King!"

The crowd of people grew very angry at this, 5 and they shouted out, "This is an Englishman! He has come here to make trouble! Take him away! Take him away!"

Chapter 5

The man with the big hat then asked Rip again, "Why have you come here? Who are you looking for?"

Poor Rip only said, "I am looking for my neighbours. They used to spend their time here at the inn."

"Well, who are your neighbours? Tell me their names!"

Rip thought for a moment, then asked, "Where is Nicholas Vedder?"

Nobody said anything for a moment. Then an old man with a high little voice said, "Nicholas Vedder? He died eighteen years ago!"

"Where is Brom Dutcher, then?" asked Rip Van Winkle.

"Oh, he went off to fight in the war," said one of the men. "He never came back again."

"Well, where is Van Bummel the teacher?"

"Oh, he is a great man now. He is now in Congress."

Rip's heart sank when he heard of these changes in his home and friends. Now, he saw, he was alone in the world. He could not understand what the man was talking about. So many years seemed to have passed. These people spoke of matters which he could not understand: war, the election, parties, Congress.

So then poor Rip just cried out, "Does nobody here know Rip Van Winkle?"

"Oh! Rip Van Winkle?" cried two or three people. "Oh yes, there is Rip Van Winkle, over there, sitting with his back against that tree."

Rip turned and looked. What did he see? He saw a young man who looked just like himself. Just like himself, that is, when he went up the mountain the day before.

"Whatever has happened?" said Rip to himself. "If that young man is Rip Van Winkle, then who am I? Am I Rip Van Winkle, or am I some other man?"

And he held his poor head in his hands.

* * *

As Rip was thinking of these things, the man in the big hat spoke to him again.

"Who are you?" asked the man in the big hat. "What is your name?"

5 "I don't know," answered Rip, holding his head in his hands again. "I just don't know. I am not myself – I am that man over there! No: that man is somebody standing in my shoes! I was myself last night; but then I slept on the 10 mountain. And they have changed my gun. Everything has changed – I have changed! I don't know what my name is, and I don't know who I am!"

The people in the crowd now began to look at 15 each other, and they put their fingers to their heads.

"There is something wrong with that old man's head," the people said quietly to each other. "We ought to take his gun away from 20 him."

* * *

At that very moment, a young woman pushed her way to the front of the crowd. When she got there, she looked hard at the old man with his grey beard. She had a little child in her arms. 25 The child took one look at old Rip and began to cry.

"Be quiet, Rip," the mother said kindly to her child. "Don't worry. Don't be afraid of the old man."

Rip heard the name of the child, and he looked at the mother. He listened to the mother's voice. And then, little by little, Rip began to remember.

"What is your name, my good woman?" asked Rip.

"Judith Gardenier," answered the woman.

"And your father's name?" asked Rip.

"Ah, poor man!" said the woman. "Rip Van Winkle was my father's name. But he went away from home twenty years ago. Rip Van Winkle left home with his gun and his dog, and no one has heard of him since. His dog came home without him. At that time, I was just a little girl."

* * *

"And where," asked Rip at last, "where is your mother?"

"Oh, my mother," answered the young woman. "Well, a man came to the door to sell her some fish. My mother grew very angry with the man. In the end, she grew so angry that she just fell down dead."

"Well," thought Rip to himself, "that at least will make life easier for me."

Then Rip stepped forward and took his daughter and her child in his arms.

"I am your father!" cried Rip. "Once I was young Rip Van Winkle – now I am old Rip Van Winkle! Does nobody know poor Rip Van Winkle?"

Everyone stood around in great surprise for a minute or two. Just then, an old woman walked slowly out from the crowd, came up to Rip, and looked hard at him. After a moment she smiled and spoke.

"Of course!" she said. "This is Rip Van Winkle sure enough. Welcome home again, old neighbour! Wherever have you been for the past twenty years?"

It did not take Rip long to tell his story. To him, all those twenty years were like one night. The neighbours looked hard at him while he told his story. Some of them looked at each other, said a few quiet words and shook their heads. "There is something wrong with his head, poor man," they said to each other again.

* * *

Another old man now came slowly walking up the street. This was Peter Vanderdonk. He knew all about the village, and about everything that had ever happened there. Peter at once remembered Rip. What Rip had told the people, Peter said, was quite true. And Peter began to tell the crowd about the Catskill Mountains.

5   The Catskills, said old Peter Vanderdonk, were very strange mountains. Sometimes, he said, ghosts came to stay up in the Catskills. One of these ghosts was the ghost of Henry Hudson.

10   Captain Henry Hudson had sailed to America from England with some Dutchmen in a ship called the Half Moon. That was in the year 1609. After a long time, Hudson and his men had found the river and the country near

15   it. Once every twenty years, Henry Hudson came back with his men to spend the night in the Catskill Mountains. Hudson liked to look at the river that was now called by his name.

"My own father," said Peter Vanderdonk,

20   "once saw Henry Hudson and all his men playing ninepins, up near the top of the mountain. And one afternoon, I myself heard the sound of the wooden balls, like a thunderstorm far away."

* * *

25   To make a long story short – the people in the crowd went home, and there they talked about

the more important matters of the election.

Rip's daughter Judith took him home to live with her. She had a fine big house, and her husband was a fat happy man from the village. Rip remembered this man as one of the little boys who used to fly kites.

Rip's son was the young man who had been sitting with his back against the tree. The young man had work to do in the fields, but in this matter he was just like his father. He was always ready to help a neighbour, even in the hardest work. But work in his own fields – that was something he just could not do.

Chapter 6

Rip now began to talk to people and to walk through the village just as before. He soon found many of his friends from the old days. But these friends too, of course, had grown much older, so Rip made new friends among the younger people. They all liked him very much.

Rip had no work to do at home. A man of Rip's age does not have to work, so he went down the street and sat outside the inn. People loved to hear his stories of the old times before the war.

They then told Rip about the past few years. They told him of the strange things that had happened while he had been sleeping. At first, Rip could not understand the things they said. Bit by bit, he came to see more clearly. There had been a great war, they said. In that war, America had made itself free from England. Rip was no longer living under King George the Third, he was now a free man living in the United States of America.

These were matters of history and politics. Rip was not really interested in politics.

In one way, though, Rip was interested in being free. For a long time, he had wanted to be free from his sharp-tongued wife. And now he was free from her. Now, he could go in and out of the house whenever he wanted to. There was no sharp tongue to call him back.

Every time someone spoke of Rip's wife, Rip shook his head and turned his eyes up towards the sky. And what did he mean by that? Nobody knew.

* * *

Rip now told his story to everyone who came to the Union Hotel. Rip's story was the very same story that I have just told you. Some people did not really believe it. But the old Dutch people of the village believed the story. Even today, when they hear thunder over the Catskill Mountains, people say, "Listen! That's Captain Henry Hudson and his men, playing ninepins!"

There are still wives in the village who have sharp tongues which they use against their husbands. And sometimes one of those husbands shakes his head, turns his eyes up towards the sky, and says, "I'd love a drink from Rip Van Winkle's barrel!"

Chapter 1

1. Say three things about the Catskill Mountains.

2. How do the people in the village feel about Rip Van Winkle?

3. What sort of work does Rip like doing?

4. What sort of work do you like doing?

Chapter 2

1. What is Rip's wife like?

2. What do the men talk about outside the inn?

3. Where does Rip go with his dog?

4. Do you have a dog, a cat or some other animal? If so, talk about it.

Chapter 3

1. What does Rip hear just as he is starting on his way down the mountain?

2. Where do Rip and the little old man go with the barrel?

3. Talk about the men who are playing ninepins: look at the picture.

4. What happens to Rip's gun?

5. Why do you think Rip finds it difficult to move?

6. Have you ever slept outside? If so, say what happened.

Chapter 4

1. What does Rip notice about the houses in the village?

2. What is Rip's own house like?

3. What has happened to the head on the sign of the inn?

4. Why are the people in the crowd angry?

5. Have you ever seen an angry crowd? If so, say what happened.

Chapter 5

1. What has happened to Rip's three old neighbours?

2. What do the people think about Rip Van Winkle?

3. Who is the young woman with the child?

4. What has happened to Rip's wife?

5. What does Peter Vanderdonk say about Henry Hudson?

6. Where does Rip go to live?

7. What more can you find out about Henry Hudson?

Chapter 6

1. What do the people tell Rip about the past few years?

2. Which of the people believe Rip's story?

3. Have you read this story before, in your own language?

4. Now, how about reading this story in the original, as Washington Irving wrote it?

Chapter 1

1.1.
Look at the first part of this chapter and find words which mean the opposite of:

low
up
new

1.2.
Look at the map on page **4**. How far is it from New York City to Catskill?

Chapter 2

Adverbs

2.1.
Adverbs are often formed by adding -ly to the adjective. At the start of Chapter 2, you can see the adverb "usually". Write down all the adverbs ending in -ly that you can find in this chapter.

2.2.
Look at the map on page 4, then draw and colour a map of your own.

Chapter 3

3.1.
Find 3 words of sound, 3 words of colour and 3 words of movement in the first part of this chapter.

3.2.
Find a modern map of the Hudson River, then write in new places and roads on your own map.

Chapter 4

4.1.
Look at the first part of this chapter and find words which mean the opposite of:

small
new
loud
short
fat

4.2.

Look at an atlas. How far are the Catskill Mountains from your own home?

Chapter 5

5.1.

Just suppose:

You go to sleep this evening and sleep for twenty years. What will the world be like then?
   Write down some changes in:

- the place where you live
- your neighbours
- your friends
- your family

5.2.

Plan a journey from your own home to Rip Van Winkle's home.

Chapter 6

6.1.
Make a list of countries that have changed their names.

6.2.
Plan a three-day visit to the Hudson River.